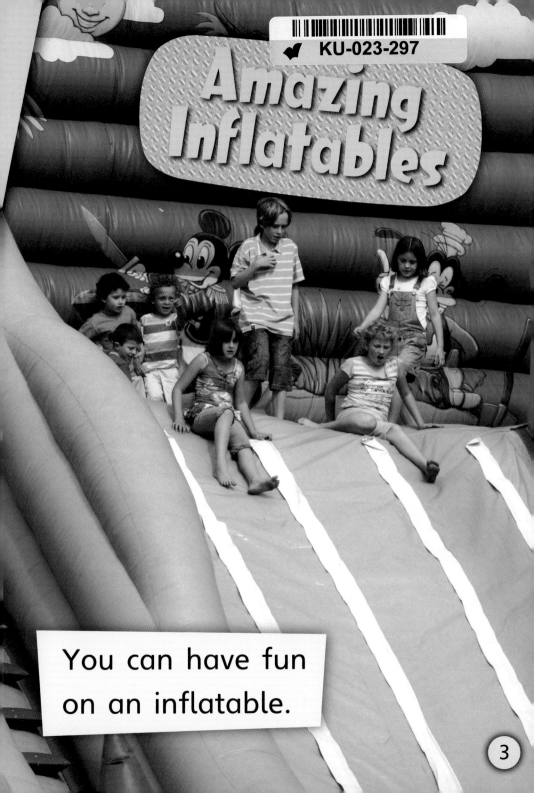

Amazing Inflatables

You can have fun
on an inflatable.

Look at this!

It is an inflatable castle.

BLOW UP!

Dee Reid

**Story illustrated by
Tom Percival**

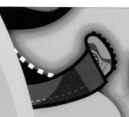

Heinemann

 **Before Reading**

Find out about

•Some amazing inflatables

Tricky words

• inflatable
• castle
• suit

Introduce these tricky words and help the reader when they come across them later!

Text starter

There are some amazing inflatables, including an inflatable castle, an inflatable ship, and even an inflatable suit. You can play with these inflatables and have fun.

You can play in this castle and have fun.

This inflatable is cool.

Look at this!

It is an inflatable ship.

You can play in this ship and have fun.

This inflatable is cool.

Look at this!

It is an inflatable suit.

You can play in this suit and have fun.

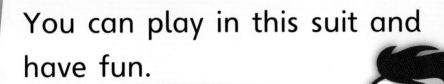

Would you like to wear a suit like this?

This inflatable is cool.

Inflatables are fun.

Quiz

Text Detective

- Which inflatable do you think looks the most exciting?
- Why do you think it is fun to go on an inflatable?

Word Detective

- **Phonic Focus:** Initial phonemes

  Page 8: Find a word that starts with the phoneme 'a'.
- Page 5: Find a word that rhymes with 'pool'.
- Page 5: Count the words in the first sentence.

Super Speller

Read this word:

at

Now try to spell it!

HA! HA! HA!

Q What's yellow and white and goes up and down?

A An egg sandwich on a bouncy castle!

11

Before Reading

In this story

 Rusty

 The man

Tricky words

- pumped
- tyre
- bigger
- didn't
- blew

Introduce these tricky words and help the reader when they come across them later!

Story starter

Rusty is a robot. He is old and rusty but he likes to help people. One day, Rusty saw a motorbike which had a flat tyre.

Rusty and the Flat Tyre

"Can I help you?" said Rusty.

"Yes," said the man.
"You can help."

Rusty pumped the tyre.
Rusty pumped and pumped.

What do you think will happen next?

The tyre got bigger and bigger.

"Stop!" said the man.

But Rusty didn't stop.

Rusty pumped and pumped.

The tyre got bigger and bigger.

"Stop! Stop!" said the man.

The tyre blew up.

"You rusty tin can,"
said the man.
"You blew up the tyre."

Quiz

- What did Rusty do wrong when he tried to help the man?
- Why do you think Rusty didn't stop when the man asked him to stop?

Word Detective

- **Phonic Focus: Initial phonemes**

  Page 17: Find a word beginning with the phoneme 'm'.
- Page 15: Find the word 'pumped' three times.
- Page 16: Find a word that means 'larger'.

Super Speller

Read this word:

up

Now try to spell it!

HA! HA! HA!

Q What do you get if you cross a broomstick with a motorbike?

A A broom, broom, broomstick.